Match each picture to the letter it starts

g   k   l   p

d   n   w   u

Colour the pictures.

Eddy has drawn some pictures for you to colour.
Trace over the words.

ring

fish

hat

apple

gate

lorry

Write these words.

gate   gate   gate

fish   fish   fish

4

Draw a line to match each letter to the thing that begins with that letter.

q

d

f

p

i

j

Look at the picture and think of the word.
Write in each box the letter that starts the word.

k   l   m   n   o

Colour the pictures.

Cross out the odd one out in each line.

bee   bee   bee   bed   bee

fly   fly   fly   flag   fly

egg   egg   eye   egg   egg

man   man   man   mat   man

ten   tin   ten   ten   ten

Trace over these words.

bee   bee   bee   bee

egg   egg   egg   egg

man   man   man   man

Eddy has found an alphabet caterpillar.
Trace over the letters.

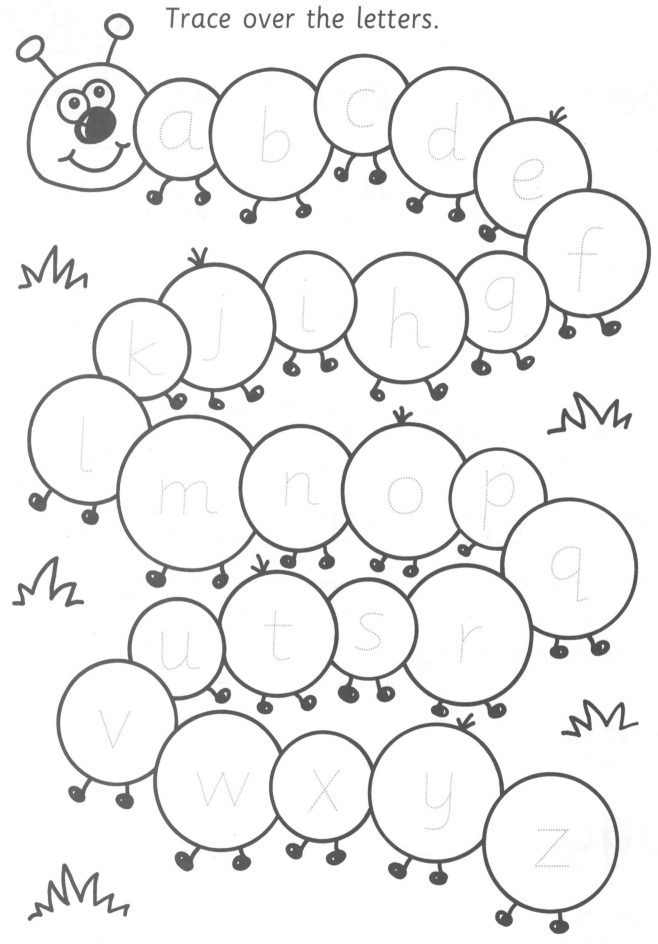

Draw a line to match each letter to the thing
that begins with that letter.

z

b

w

r

o

g

Colour Eddy's picture using the colour that goes with each letter.

i = yellow   j = green   k = pink   l = brown

m = purple   n = grey   o = orange   p = red

Cross out the odd one out in each line.

jam jam jar jam jam

leg leg leg log leg

hot hat hot hot hot

net net nut net net

sand sand sand sand sat

Trace over these words.

net net net net

hot hot hot hot

sat sat sat sat

11

Look at each picture and think of the word.

Match each picture to the letter that it begins with.

Colour the pictures.

Eddy has made some counters to show numbers.

Join the pairs that show the same number.

Colour each pair the same colour.

Eddy has found some letter insects.
Trace over the letters.

Colour the **q** insects green.

Colour the **r** insects yellow.

Colour the **v** insects purple.

Colour the **x** insects brown.

Colour the **p** insects orange.

Colour the **a** insects pink.

Draw a ring around the word that matches the picture.

egg

bat

hat
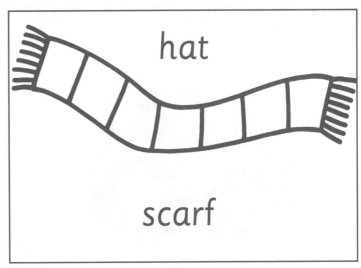
scarf

zip
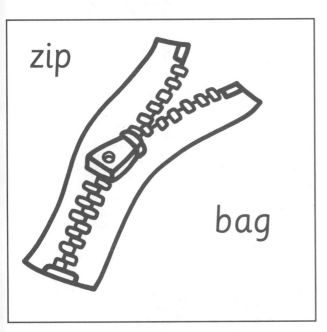
bag

bee

worm

gate

dog

car

tap

Colour the pictures.

Look at the picture and think of the word.
Write in each box the letter that starts the word.

p q r s t

Colour the pictures.

Eddy has an alphabet jigsaw.

Trace over the letters.

Join the letters in the right order.

a b c d e f

i k j l h g

m n o p q

u t s r

v

w x y z

Can you find another word the same as the one in the box? Draw a ring around it.

 ball    car    car   ball    car

 hat    hat   dog   dog   dog

 key    bat   bat    bat    key

 doll    door   door    doll   door

Trace over these words.

dog   dog   dog   dog

bat   bat   bat   bat

doll   doll   doll   doll

Eddy's cards have words on them.
Join the words that are the same.

Colour each pair the same colour.

Draw a ring around the word that matches the picture.

pen

apple

flower

tree

mouse

cat

gate

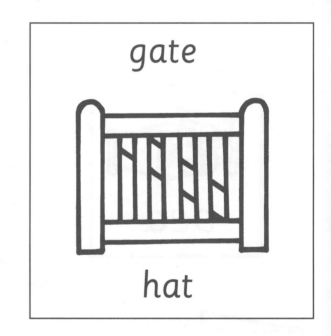

hat

sun

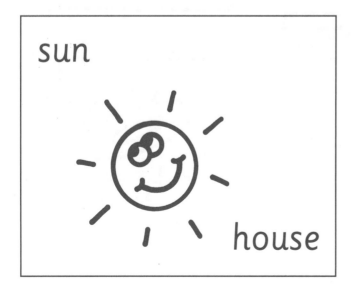

house

man

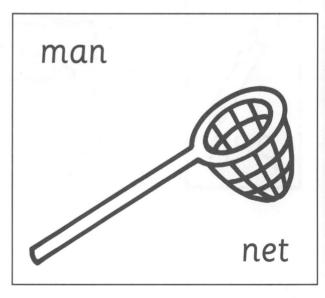

net

Colour the pictures.

Eddy has written some words on cards.

Trace over the words.

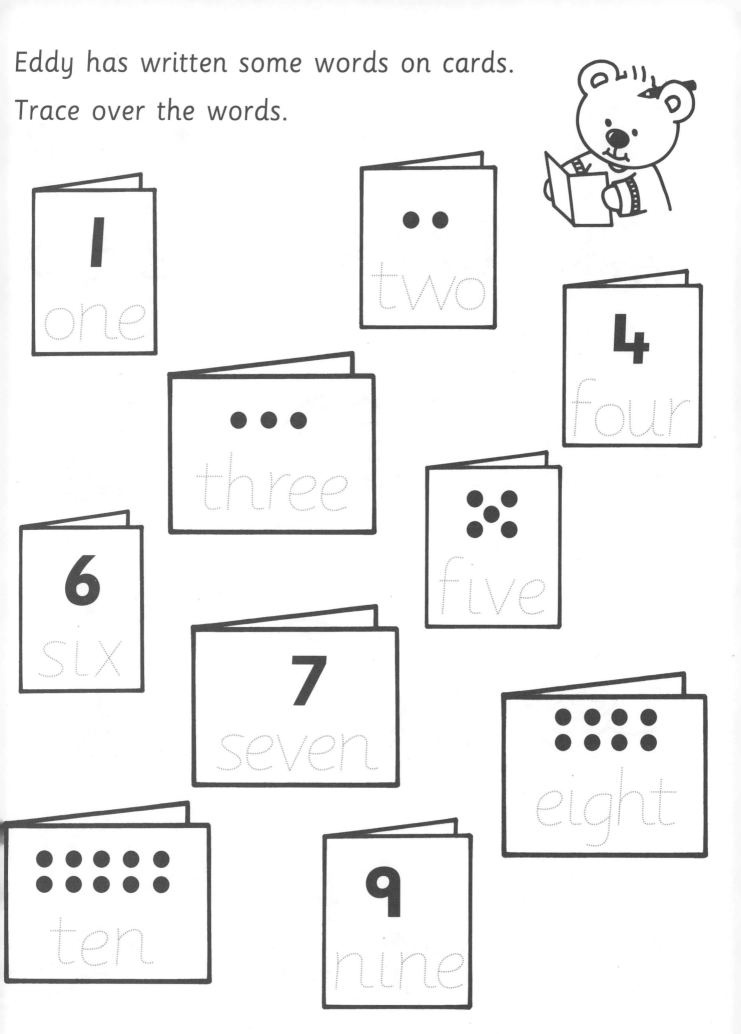

Can you join the cards in the right order?

Eddy has drawn some pictures for you to colour.
Trace over the words.

ant   ball   car   dog

hat   igloo   jam

orange   pen   queen

umbrella   van   watch